Times Table Practice

A LAUGHING LOBSTER BOOK 978-1-910765-75-3

Published in Great Britain by Laughing Lobster
an imprint of Centum Publishing Ltd.
This edition published 2021.
3 5 7 9 10 8 6 4 2

Illustrations by Louise Gardner.

Laughing Lobster an imprint of Centum Publishing Ltd, 20 Devon Square,
Newton Abbot, Devon, TQ12 2HR, UK
Centum Publishing Ltd, 9/10 Fenian St, Dublin 2, D02 RX24, Ireland
books@centumpublishingltd.co.uk
LAUGHING LOBSTER AN IMPRINT OF CENTUM PUBLISHING
Limited Reg. No. 08497203

A CIP catalogue record for this book is available from the British Library.

Printed in China.

Answers are at the back of the book!

About this book

The activities in this book will help your child to learn their times tables, from 2 to 12. The book is also packed with lots of fun reinforcement activities to help build confidence and recall.

Before you start:

1. Find a quiet place for you and your child to work, preferably at a table.

2. Make sure your child learns to hold a pencil correctly. This will make learning easier for them, and give them the confidence to form the answers.

3. Always give your child plenty of praise and encouragement. They don't have to complete each page in one go. Stop or move onto another page if they get tired or distracted.

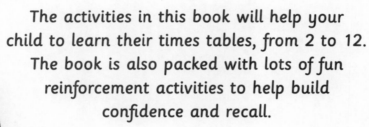

Counting in Twos

Hi, my name is Mia! Learn to count in twos with me and Mops the bunny. Each bunny has two ears. How many ears are there altogether? The first one is done for you.

Example:

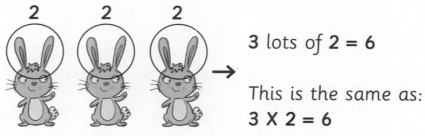

3 lots of **2** = **6**

This is the same as:
3 X 2 = 6

Now try these:

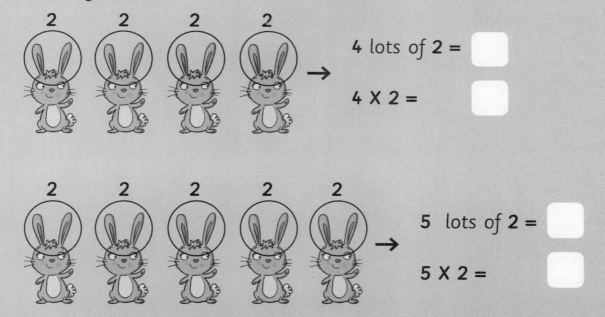

4 lots of **2** = ☐

4 X 2 = ☐

5 lots of **2** = ☐

5 X 2 = ☐

Can you count in twos on this number line? I've started it off for you.

0 1 **2** 3 **4** 5 **6** 7 8 9 10 11 12 13 14 15 16 17 18 19 20 21 22 23 24

This is the two times table! Let's write it on the next page.

The 2 Times Table

Let's trace the 2 times table in the first column, then write it again in the second.

1 x 2 = 2	
2 x 2 = 4	
3 x 2 = 6	
4 x 2 = 8	
5 x 2 = 10	
6 x 2 = 12	
7 x 2 = 14	
8 x 2 = 16	
9 x 2 = 18	
10 x 2 = 20	
11 x 2 = 22	
12 x 2 = 24	

4

Twos in a Muddle

Mop has got the answers to Mia's 2 times table problems in a muddle. Can you match the problems to the correct answers? Draw lines between the problems and the answers.

2 x 2 =

4 x 2 =

7 x 2 =

9 x 2 =

10 x 2 =

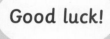

Good luck!

Counting in Fives

Hi there, my name is Joe! Learn to count in fives with me. Each flower has five petals. How many petals are there altogether? The first one is done for you.

Example:

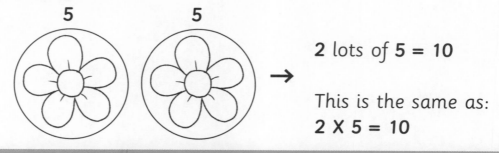

2 lots of **5 = 10**

This is the same as:
2 X 5 = 10

Now try these:

4 lots of **5** = ☐

4 X 5 = ☐

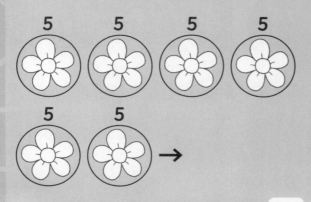

5 lots of **5** = ☐

5 X 5 = ☐

Can you count in fives in this number grid? Shade in the numbers as you count in fives. I've started it off for you.

1	2	3	4	5	6	7	8	9	10
11	12	13	14	15	16	17	18	19	20
21	22	23	24	25	26	27	28	29	30
31	32	33	34	35	36	37	38	39	40
41	42	43	44	45	46	47	48	49	50
51	52	53	54	55	56	57	58	59	60
61	62	63	64	65	66	67	68	69	70
71	72	73	74	75	76	77	78	79	80
81	82	83	84	85	86	87	88	89	90
91	92	93	94	95	96	97	98	99	100

This is the five times table!
Let's write it on the next page.

The 5 Times Table

Let's trace the 5 times table in the first column, then write it again in the second.

1 x 5 = 5	
2 x 5 = 10	
3 x 5 = 15	
4 x 5 = 20	
5 x 5 = 25	
6 x 5 = 30	
7 x 5 = 35	
8 x 5 = 40	
9 x 5 = 45	
10 x 5 = 50	
11 x 5 = 55	
12 x 5 = 60	

7

Missing Fives

Uh-oh! Dudley has chewed off some of the numbers from these multiplication problems. Can you help Joe fill in the blanks?

Woof!

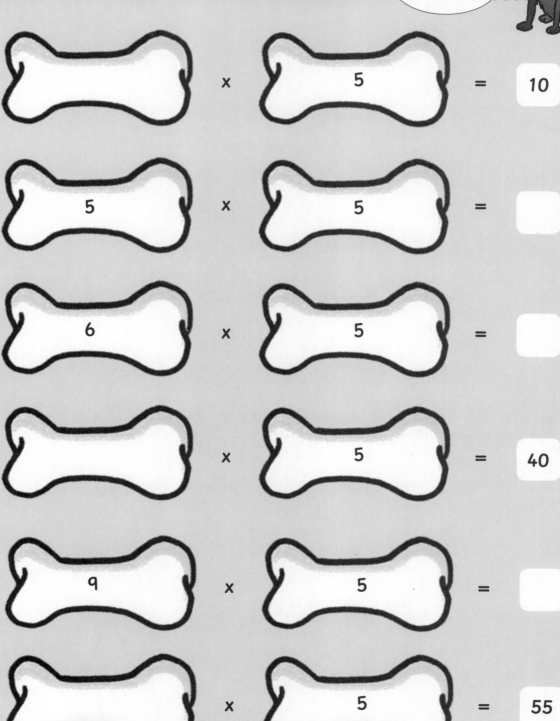

___ x 5 = 10

5 x 5 = ___

6 x 5 = ___

___ x 5 = 40

9 x 5 = ___

___ x 5 = 55

Counting in Tens

Hello, my name is Noah! Learn to count in tens with me. Each tree has ten birds resting in it. How many birds are there altogether? The first one is done for you.

Example:

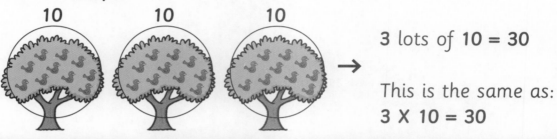

3 lots of 10 = 30

This is the same as:
3 X 10 = 30

Now try these:

4 lots of 10 = ☐

4 X 10 = ☐

5 lots of 10 = ☐

5 X 10 = ☐

Can you count in tens in this number grid? Shade in the numbers as you count in tens. I've started it off for you.

1	2	3	4	5	6	7	8	9	10
11	12	13	14	15	16	17	18	19	20
21	22	23	24	25	26	27	28	29	30
31	32	33	34	35	36	37	38	39	40
41	42	43	44	45	46	47	48	49	50
51	52	53	54	55	56	57	58	59	60
61	62	63	64	65	66	67	68	69	70
71	72	73	74	75	76	77	78	79	80
81	82	83	84	85	86	87	88	89	90
91	92	93	94	95	96	97	98	99	100
101	102	103	104	105	106	107	108	109	110
111	112	113	114	115	116	117	118	119	120

This is the ten times table! Let's write it on the next page.

The 10 Times Table

Let's trace the 10 times table in the first column, then write it again in the second.

1 x 10 = 10

2 x 10 = 20

3 x 10 = 30

4 x 10 = 40

5 x 10 = 50

6 x 10 = 60

7 x 10 = 70

8 x 10 = 80

9 x 10 = 90

10 x 10 = 100

11 x 10 = 110

12 x 10 = 120

10 Times Table Trees

These 10 times table trees have dropped the leaves with the right answers to the problems. Circle the leaf that contains the correct answer for each tree.

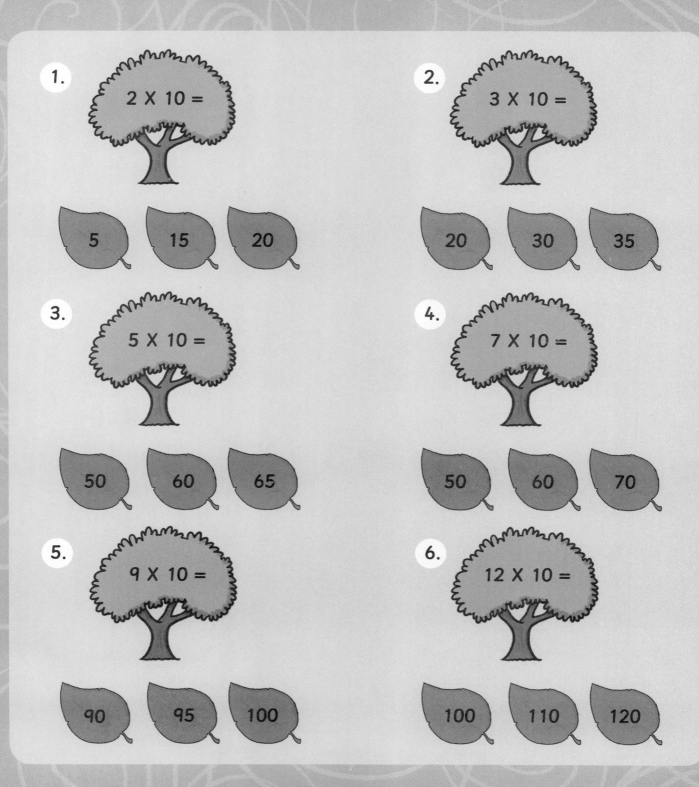

1. 2 X 10 =

5   15   20

2. 3 X 10 =

20   30   35

3. 5 X 10 =

50   60   65

4. 7 X 10 =

50   60   70

5. 9 X 10 =

90   95   100

6. 12 X 10 =

100   110   120

Counting in Threes

Hi, my name is Poppy! Learn to count in threes with me. Each group has three carrots. How many carrots are there altogether? The first one is done for you.

Example:

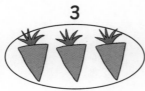

3 lots of **3** = 9

This is the same as:
3 X 3 = 9

Now try these:

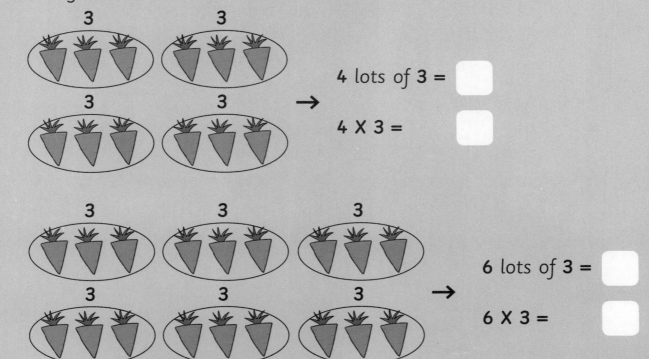

4 lots of **3** = ☐

4 X 3 = ☐

6 lots of **3** = ☐

6 X 3 = ☐

Can you count in threes on this number line? I've started it off for you.

0 1 2 3 4 5 6 7 8 9 10 11 12 13 14 15 16 17 18

19 20 21 22 23 24 25 26 27 28 29 30 31 32 33 34 35 36

This is the three times table! Let's write it on the next page.

The 3 Times Table

Let's trace the 3 times table in the first column,
then write it again in the second.

1 x 3 = 3

2 x 3 = 6

3 x 3 = 9

4 x 3 = 12

5 x 3 = 15

6 x 3 = 18

7 x 3 = 21

8 x 3 = 24

9 x 3 = 27

10 x 3 = 30

11 x 3 = 33

12 x 3 = 36

Odd Socks

There are 3 socks in each group. Count the sock groups to work out the answers to these problems from the 3 times table.

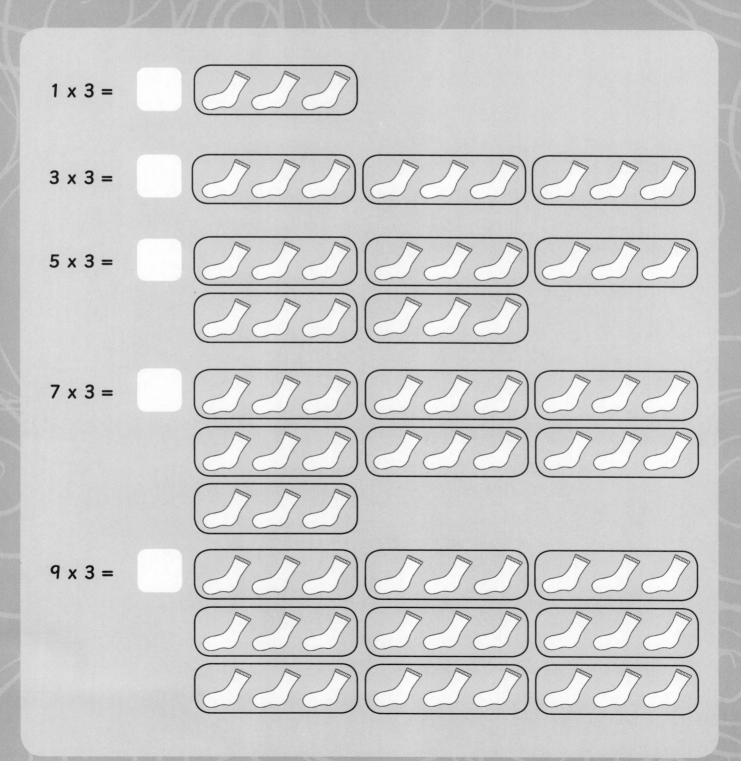

1 x 3 = ☐

3 x 3 = ☐

5 x 3 = ☐

7 x 3 = ☐

9 x 3 = ☐

Counting in Fours

Hello, I'm Harry and this is Dudley the dog! Learn to count in fours with us. Each bowl has four apples. How many apples are there altogether? The first one is done for you.

Example:

4   4   4

→

3 lots of 4 = 12

This is the same as:
3 X 4 = 12

Now try these:

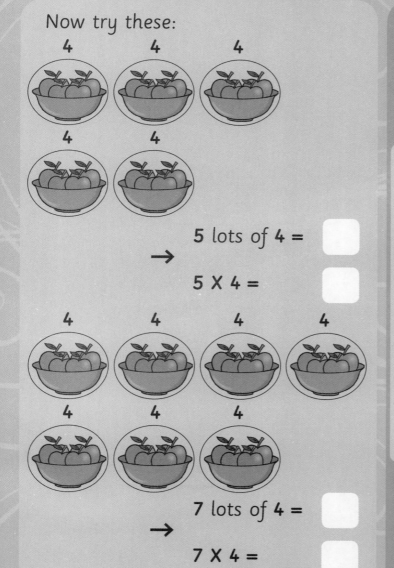

4   4   4

4   4

5 lots of 4 = ☐

→

5 X 4 = ☐

4   4   4   4

4   4   4

7 lots of 4 = ☐

→

7 X 4 = ☐

Can you count in fours in this number grid? Shade in the numbers as you count in fours. I've started it off for you.

1	2	3	4	5	6	7	8	9	10
11	12	13	14	15	16	17	18	19	20
21	22	23	24	25	26	27	28	29	30
31	32	33	34	35	36	37	38	39	40
41	42	43	44	45	46	47	48	49	50
51	52	53	54	55	56	57	58	59	60
61	62	63	64	65	66	67	68	69	70
71	72	73	74	75	76	77	78	79	80
81	82	83	84	85	86	87	88	89	90
91	92	93	94	95	96	97	98	99	100

This is the four times table! Let's write it on the next page.

The 4 Times Table

Let's trace the 4 times table in the first column, then write it again in the second.

1 x 4 = 4	
2 x 4 = 8	
3 x 4 = 12	
4 x 4 = 16	
5 x 4 = 20	
6 x 4 = 24	
7 x 4 = 28	
8 x 4 = 32	
9 x 4 = 36	
10 x 4 = 40	
11 x 4 = 44	
12 x 4 = 48	

Catching Times Tables

Harry is throwing balls to Dudley. Which ball should he throw to complete the 4 times table problems? Draw a line from the correct ball to the answer box and write your answer.

12   14   13   3 x 4 = ☐

24   20   26   5 x 4 = ☐

27   26   28   7 x 4 = ☐

40   44   48   10 x 4 = ☐

50   48   58   12 x 4 ☐

Counting in Sixes

Wow, you're doing so great. Let's continue learning! This time, let's learn to count in sixes together. Each group has six leaves. How many leaves are there altogether? The first one is done for you.

Example:

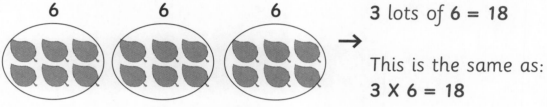

6   6   6   →   3 lots of 6 = 18

This is the same as:
3 X 6 = 18

Now try these:

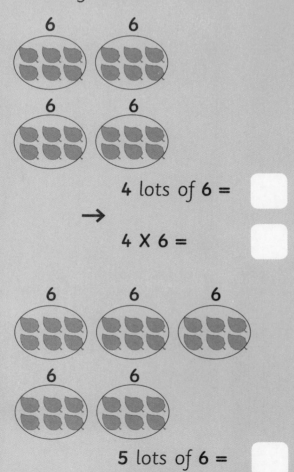

6   6

6   6

4 lots of 6 =

→

4 X 6 =

6   6   6

6   6

5 lots of 6 =

→

5 X 6 =

Can you count in sixes in this number grid? Shade in the numbers as you count in sixes. I've started it off for you.

1	2	3	4	5	6	7	8	9	10	11	12
13	14	15	16	17	18	19	20	21	22	23	24
25	26	27	28	29	30	31	32	33	34	35	36
37	38	39	40	41	42	43	44	45	46	47	48
49	50	51	52	53	54	55	56	57	58	59	60
61	62	63	64	65	66	67	68	69	70	71	72
73	74	75	76	77	78	79	80	81	82	83	84
85	86	87	88	89	90	91	92	93	94	95	96
97	98	99	100	101	102	103	104	105	106	107	108
109	110	111	112	113	114	115	116	117	118	119	120
121	122	123	124	125	126	127	128	129	130	131	132
133	134	135	136	137	138	139	140	141	142	143	144

This is the six times table!
Let's write it on the next page.

The 6 Times Table

Let's trace the 6 times table in the first column, then write it again in the second.

1 x 6 = 6	
2 x 6 = 12	
3 x 6 = 18	
4 x 6 = 24	
5 x 6 = 30	
6 x 6 = 36	
7 x 6 = 42	
8 x 6 = 48	
9 x 6 = 54	
10 x 6 = 60	
11 x 6 = 66	
12 x 6 = 72	

19

Sweet Sixes

In each of these sweet problems the first number is missing. Can you complete the problems?

x 6 = 30

x 6 = 6

x 6 = 24

x 6 = 66

x 6 = 36

x 6 = 42

x 6 = 18

x 6 = 54

x 6 = 60

x 6 = 72

x 6 = 48

x 6 = 12

Counting in Sevens

Go, you! The seven times table can be tricky, but let's learn it together. Each sock has seven spots. How many spots are there altogether? The first one is done for you.

Example:

7   7

 →

2 lots of 7 = 14

This is the same as:
2 X 7 = 14

Now try these:

7   7   7

7   7   7

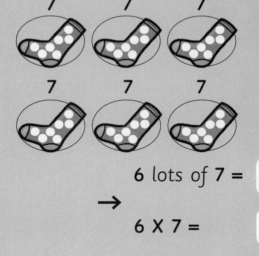

6 lots of 7 = ☐

→

6 X 7 = ☐

7   7   7

7   7   7

7

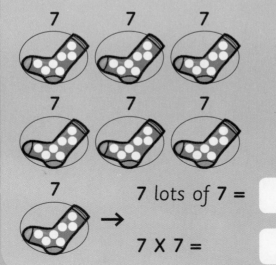

7 lots of 7 = ☐

→

7 X 7 = ☐

Can you count in sevens in this number grid? Shade in the numbers as you count in sevens. I've started it off for you.

1	2	3	4	5	6	7	8	9	10	11	12
13	14	15	16	17	18	19	20	21	22	23	24
25	26	27	28	29	30	31	32	33	34	35	36
37	38	39	40	41	42	43	44	45	46	47	48
49	50	51	52	53	54	55	56	57	58	59	60
61	62	63	64	65	66	67	68	69	70	71	72
73	74	75	76	77	78	79	80	81	82	83	84
85	86	87	88	89	90	91	92	93	94	95	96
97	98	99	100	101	102	103	104	105	106	107	108
109	110	111	112	113	114	115	116	117	118	119	120
121	122	123	124	125	126	127	128	129	130	131	132
133	134	135	136	137	138	139	140	141	142	143	144

This is the seven times table!
Let's write it on the next page.

The 7 Times Table

Let's trace the 7 times table in the first column,
then write it again in the second.

1 x 7 = 7	
2 x 7 = 14	
3 x 7 = 21	
4 x 7 = 28	
5 x 7 = 35	
6 x 7 = 42	
7 x 7 = 49	
8 x 7 = 56	
9 x 7 = 63	
10 x 7 = 70	
11 x 7 = 77	
12 x 7 = 84	

22

Fruity Sevens

Joe has some fruity 7 times table problems and Poppy has the answers. Can you draw lines to match the bananas to the oranges and solve the problems below?

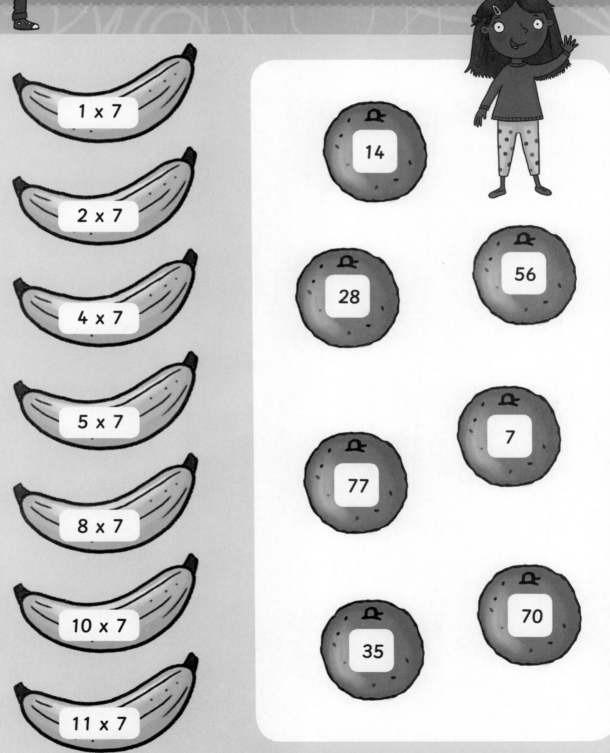

1 x 7

2 x 7

4 x 7

5 x 7

8 x 7

10 x 7

11 x 7

14

28

56

7

77

35

70

Counting in Eights

Hey! How is it going so far? Ready to learn the eight times table? Each bag has eight apples. How many apples are there altogether? The first one is done for you.

Example:

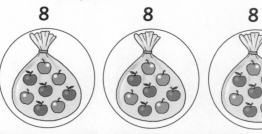

8   8   8

→

3 lots of **8** = **24**

This is the same as:

3 X 8 = 24

Now try these:

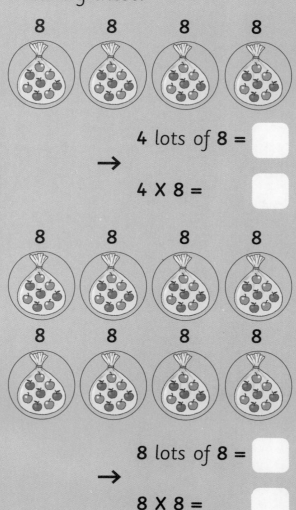

8   8   8   8

4 lots of **8** = ☐

→

4 X 8 = ☐

8   8   8   8

8   8   8   8

8 lots of **8** = ☐

→

8 X 8 = ☐

Can you count in eights in this number grid? Shade in the numbers as you count in eights. I've started it off for you.

1	2	3	4	5	6	7	8	9	10	11	12
13	14	15	16	17	18	19	20	21	22	23	24
25	26	27	28	29	30	31	32	33	34	35	36
37	38	39	40	41	42	43	44	45	46	47	48
49	50	51	52	53	54	55	56	57	58	59	60
61	62	63	64	65	66	67	68	69	70	71	72
73	74	75	76	77	78	79	80	81	82	83	84
85	86	87	88	89	90	91	92	93	94	95	96
97	98	99	100	101	102	103	104	105	106	107	108
109	110	111	112	113	114	115	116	117	118	119	120
121	122	123	124	125	126	127	128	129	130	131	132
133	134	135	136	137	138	139	140	141	142	143	144

This is the eight times table! Let's write it on the next page.

The 8 Times Table

Let's trace the 8 times table in the first column, then write it again in the second.

1 x 8 = 8	
2 x 8 = 16	
3 x 8 = 24	
4 x 8 = 32	
5 x 8 = 40	
6 x 8 = 48	
7 x 8 = 56	
8 x 8 = 64	
9 x 8 = 72	
10 x 8 = 80	
11 x 8 = 88	
12 x 8 = 96	

Bouncing About

Can you help Noah practise the eight times table by drawing lines to match each problem to the correct answer on a ball?

24

2 x 8 =

88

11 x 8 =

6 x 8 =

16

40

3 x 8 =

5 x 8 =

72

9 x 8 =

48

Counting in Nines

Hey, again! Time to tackle the nine times table. Let's go! Learn to count in nines with me. Each group has nine eggs. How many eggs are there altogether? The first one is done for you.

Example:

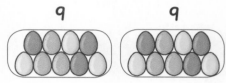

→ 4 lots of **9** = 36

This is the same as:
4 X **9** = 36

Now try these:

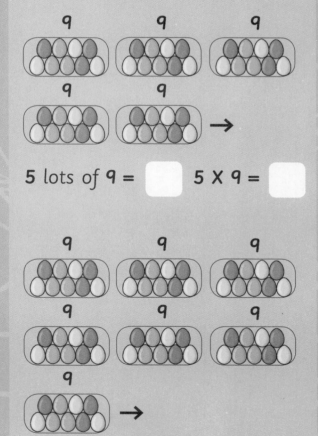

5 lots of **9** = ☐   5 X **9** = ☐

7 lots of **9** = ☐

7 X **9** = ☐

Can you count in nines in this number grid? Shade in the numbers as you count in nines. I've started it off for you.

1	2	3	4	5	6	7	8	9	10	11	12
13	14	15	16	17	18	19	20	21	22	23	24
25	26	27	28	29	30	31	32	33	34	35	36
37	38	39	40	41	42	43	44	45	46	47	48
49	50	51	52	53	54	55	56	57	58	59	60
61	62	63	64	65	66	67	68	69	70	71	72
73	74	75	76	77	78	79	80	81	82	83	84
85	86	87	88	89	90	91	92	93	94	95	96
97	98	99	100	101	102	103	104	105	106	107	108
109	110	111	112	113	114	115	116	117	118	119	120
121	122	123	124	125	126	127	128	129	130	131	132
133	134	135	136	137	138	139	140	141	142	143	144

This is the nine times table! Let's write it on the next page.

The 9 Times Table

Let's trace the 9 times table in the first column, then write it again in the second.

1 x 9 = 9	
2 x 9 = 18	
3 x 9 = 27	
4 x 9 = 36	
5 x 9 = 45	
6 x 9 = 54	
7 x 9 = 63	
8 x 9 = 72	
9 x 9 = 81	
10 x 9 = 90	
11 x 9 = 99	
12 x 9 = 108	

The 11 Times Table

Izzy would like to show you the 11 times table!
Let's trace the 11 times table in the first column,
then write it in the second.

1 x 11 = 11	
2 x 11 = 22	
3 x 11 = 33	
4 x 11 = 44	
5 x 11 = 55	
6 x 11 = 66	
7 x 11 = 77	
8 x 11 = 88	
9 x 11 = 99	
10 x 11 = 110	
11 x 11 = 121	
12 x 11 = 132	

The 12 Times Table

Here's Izzy again, this time with the 12 times table. Let's trace the 12 times table in the first column, then write it in the second.

1 x 12 = 12	
2 x 12 = 24	
3 x 12 = 36	
4 x 12 = 48	
5 x 12 = 60	
6 x 12 = 72	
7 x 12 = 84	
8 x 12 = 96	
9 x 12 = 108	
10 x 12 = 120	
11 x 12 = 132	
12 x 12 = 144	

Answers

Page 3 Counting in Twos
1) **8**
2) **10**

0 1 (2) 3 (4) 5 (6) 7 (8) 9 (10) 11 (12) 13 (14) 15 (16) 17 (18) 19 (20) 21 (22) 23 (24)

Page 5 Twos in a Muddle
2 x 2 = 4
4 x 2 = 8
7 x 2 = 14
9 x 2 = 18
10 x 2 = 20

Page 6 Counting in Fives
1) **20**
2) **30**

1	2	3	4	5	6	7	8	9	10
11	12	13	14	15	16	17	18	19	20
21	22	23	24	25	26	27	28	29	30
31	32	33	34	35	36	37	38	39	40
41	42	43	44	45	46	47	48	49	50
51	52	53	54	55	56	57	58	59	60
61	62	63	64	65	66	67	68	69	70
71	72	73	74	75	76	77	78	79	80
81	82	83	84	85	86	87	88	89	90
91	92	93	94	95	96	97	98	99	100

(multiples of 5 circled)

Page 8 Missing Fives
2 x 5 = 10
5 x 5 = **25**
6 x 5 = **30**
8 x 5 = 40
9 x 5 = **45**
11 x 5 = 55

Page 9 Counting in Tens
1) **40**
2) **50**

1	2	3	4	5	6	7	8	9	10
11	12	13	14	15	16	17	18	19	20
21	22	23	24	25	26	27	28	29	30
31	32	33	34	35	36	37	38	39	40
41	42	43	44	45	46	47	48	49	50
51	52	53	54	55	56	57	58	59	60
61	62	63	64	65	66	67	68	69	70
71	72	73	74	75	76	77	78	79	80
81	82	83	84	85	86	87	88	89	90
91	92	93	94	95	96	97	98	99	100
101	102	103	104	105	106	107	108	109	110
111	112	113	114	115	116	117	118	119	120

(multiples of 10 circled)

Page 11 10 Times Table Trees
1) 2 x 10 = 5, 15, **20**
2) 3 x 10 = 20, **30**, 35
3) 5 x 10 = **50**, 60, 65
4) 7 x 10 = 50, 60, **70**
5) 9 x 10 = **90**, 95, 100
6) 12 x 10 = 100, 110, **120**

Page 12 Counting in Threes
1) **12**
2) **18**

0 1 2 (3) 4 5 (6) 7 8 (9) 10 11 (12) 13 14 (15) 16 17 (18) 19 20 (21) 22 23 (24) 25 26 (27) 28 29 (30) 31 32 (33) 34 35 (36)

Page 14 Odd Socks
1 x 3 = 3 (socks)
3 x 3 = 9 (socks)
5 x 3 = 15 (socks)
7 x 3 = 21 (socks)
9 x 3 = 27 (socks)

Page 15 Counting in Fours
1) **20**
2) **28**

1	2	3	4	5	6	7	8	9	10
11	12	13	14	15	16	17	18	19	20
21	22	23	24	25	26	27	28	29	30
31	32	33	34	35	36	37	38	39	40
41	42	43	44	45	46	47	48	49	50
51	52	53	54	55	56	57	58	59	60
61	62	63	64	65	66	67	68	69	70
71	72	73	74	75	76	77	78	79	80
81	82	83	84	85	86	87	88	89	90
91	92	93	94	95	96	97	98	99	100

(multiples of 4 circled)

Page 17 Catching Times Tables
3 x 4 = (12)
5 x 4 = (20)
7 x 4 = (28)
10 x 4 = (40)
12 x 4 = (48)

Page 18 Counting in Sixes
1) **24**
2) **30**

1	2	3	4	5	6	7	8	9	10	11	12
13	14	15	16	17	18	19	20	21	22	23	24
25	26	27	28	29	30	31	32	33	34	35	36
37	38	39	40	41	42	43	44	45	46	47	48
49	50	51	52	53	54	55	56	57	58	59	60
61	62	63	64	65	66	67	68	69	70	71	72
73	74	75	76	77	78	79	80	81	82	83	84
85	86	87	88	89	90	91	92	93	94	95	96
97	98	99	100	101	102	103	104	105	106	107	108
109	110	111	112	113	114	115	116	117	118	119	120
121	122	123	124	125	126	127	128	129	130	131	132
133	134	135	136	137	138	139	140	141	142	143	144

Page 20 Sweet Sixes

5 x 6 = 30
1 x 6 = 6
4 x 6 = 24
11 x 6 = 66
6 x 6 = 36
7 x 6 = 42
3 x 6 = 18
9 x 6 = 54
10 x 6 = 60
12 x 6 = 72
8 x 6 = 48
2 x 6 = 12

Page 21 Counting in Sevens

1) 42
2) 49

1	2	3	4	5	6	7	8	9	10	11	12
13	14	15	16	17	18	19	20	21	22	23	24
25	26	27	28	29	30	31	32	33	34	35	36
37	38	39	40	41	42	43	44	45	46	47	48
49	50	51	52	53	54	55	56	57	58	59	60
61	62	63	64	65	66	67	68	69	70	71	72
73	74	75	76	77	78	79	80	81	82	83	84
85	86	87	88	89	90	91	92	93	94	95	96
97	98	99	100	101	102	103	104	105	106	107	108
109	110	111	112	113	114	115	116	117	118	119	120
121	122	123	124	125	126	127	128	129	130	131	132
133	134	135	136	137	138	139	140	141	142	143	144

Page 23 Fruity Sevens

1 x 7 = 7
2 x 7 = 14
4 x 7 = 28
5 x 7 = 35
8 x 7 = 56
10 x 7 = 70
11 x 7 = 77

Page 24 Counting in Eights

1) 32
2) 64

1	2	3	4	5	6	7	8	9	10	11	12
13	14	15	16	17	18	19	20	21	22	23	24
25	26	27	28	29	30	31	32	33	34	35	36
37	38	39	40	41	42	43	44	45	46	47	48
49	50	51	52	53	54	55	56	57	58	59	60
61	62	63	64	65	66	67	68	69	70	71	72
73	74	75	76	77	78	79	80	81	82	83	84
85	86	87	88	89	90	91	92	93	94	95	96
97	98	99	100	101	102	103	104	105	106	107	108
109	110	111	112	113	114	115	116	117	118	119	120
121	122	123	124	125	126	127	128	129	130	131	132
133	134	135	136	137	138	139	140	141	142	143	144

Page 26 Bouncing About

2 x 8 = 16
3 x 8 = 24
5 x 8 = 40
6 x 8 = 48
9 x 8 = 72
11 x 8 = 88

Page 27 Counting in Nines

1) 45
2) 63

1	2	3	4	5	6	7	8	9	10	11	12
13	14	15	16	17	18	19	20	21	22	23	24
25	26	27	28	29	30	31	32	33	34	35	36
37	38	39	40	41	42	43	44	45	46	47	48
49	50	51	52	53	54	55	56	57	58	59	60
61	62	63	64	65	66	67	68	69	70	71	72
73	74	75	76	77	78	79	80	81	82	83	84
85	86	87	88	89	90	91	92	93	94	95	96
97	98	99	100	101	102	103	104	105	106	107	108
109	110	111	112	113	114	115	116	117	118	119	120
121	122	123	124	125	126	127	128	129	130	131	132
133	134	135	136	137	138	139	140	141	142	143	144